CALENDAR MOON

CALENDAR

MOON

BY NATALIA BELTING

ILLUSTRATED BY

BERNARDA BRYSON

Holt, Rinehart and Winston

New York / Chicago / San Francisco

BOOKS BY NATALIA BELTING

Calendar Moon
The Sun is a Golden Earring
Elves and Ellefolk: *Tales of the Little People*
Indy and Mr. Lincoln
Verity Mullins and the Indian
Cat Tales

To Dorothy — a sister's gift.

The seasons were appointed, and the times,
When the earth was made, and the sky stretched over it.

Man watched the stars rise, the clustered stars,
Counted six of them, counted seven;
Gave them names: Matariki, the Watery Stars,
    the Pleiades;
Watched them rise again, welcomed their appearing.

He beheld the sun journeying,
Sliding down the sky, stopping, returning,
And the moon as it changed.

He saw the rains come, and the fields grow green;
Saw winter follow summer, the seasons repeating.
Counted from seedtime to harvest; from season to
	season
The number of new moons: twelve or thirteen.
Gave them names.

He plowed and planted,
Hunted, voyaged,
Feasted and danced,
According to the rising and setting of the stars,
According to the waxing and waning moons.

He measured his days by the moons,
And ordered his life by the calendar moon.

January

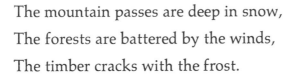

The mountain passes are deep in snow,
The forests are battered by the winds,
The timber cracks with the frost.

Ice stretches out from the river banks,
Tries to hold the running water.
The salmon are gone back to the sea,
The trout sleep beneath the cold.

Men keep to their earth lodges.
They tell the tales of their fathers.
They count the moons from the time of
    wild-berry picking,
From the first moon of their year.

They count the moons on their fingers, and name them,
Tuck the thumb into the palm,
Bend down the first finger, and the second.
They hold the third finger and give its name
    to the moon.
They say, *This is the moon-of-the-little-finger's-partner.*

       —*Klamath Indians (Northwestern United States)*

The summer corn ripens,
The wheat and the beans are ready for harvest.

There is work to be done:
Reaping and threshing,
Plowing and planting; gathering the almonds
    and cracking them,
Repairing the huts and the cattle kraals,
Building new ones.

This is the busy moon.
This is the moon-when-man-answers-a-summons,
    "I-come-directly. Have-patience. I-am-busy."
                        —*Baronga (Southeast Africa)*

The sun is coming.
In white deerskins, with many beads, and a shining
    mask hiding his face,
The sun is following the trails above the great
    waters of the sky.

Above the Mountain-Covered-with-Flaking-Stone,
    West Mountain,
And Turtle Mountain, south, the home of
    Wind Old Woman,
And Blue Stone Mountain, east,
And Bear Mountain, north, the home of
    Snow Old Man,
The sun walks the trails again.

He warms the earth for the planting of beans.
He sets the water free from the ice in the
     mountain streams.
Where it was held among the rocks, the water
     flows forth.

And the rocks tumble along the canyon walls.
Their noise sends the coyotes running.
This is the moon-when-the-coyotes-are-frightened.
                —Tewa Indians (Southwestern United States)

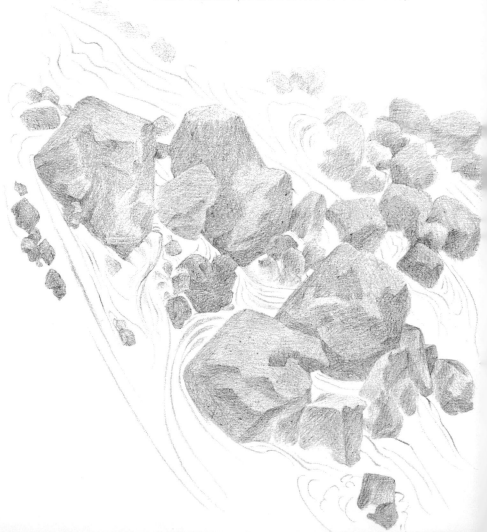

Put the pine tree in its pot by the doorway,
Set bamboo about the house,
Bring the crane and the tortoise to live in the house,
And long life and prosperity will dwell with you.

Eat beans, one more than the years of your age,
    and repeat,
"Out with the devils, in with good fortune."

Invite the ancestors to be your guests.
Set out food and drink for them.

Make calls on your friends and wish them peace
 and good health,

For this is the first moon,
The moon of three beginnings.
This is the holiday moon,
This is the friendly-moon.

—Japanese

It is time. The geese fly overhead, returning.
The snow goes away; the forest trails are uncovered.
Green streaks the willow bark; fresh-running creeks
    water the willow roots.
Hickory buds swell, and the buds of the elm
    and the ash and the oak.

It is time. Days warm, but nights spread frost,
    crisp the air with it.
Maple sap drips from the holes cut in the trunks.
It drips into birch-bark troughs.
The women collect it, pour it into great kettles,
    and boil it,
Boil it thick; cool it away from the fire;
Make hard brown cakes of maple sugar.
This is the sugar moon,
This is the moon-when-the-juice-drips-from-the-trees.
    —*Delaware Indians (Northeastern United States)*

Winter has packed her brown garments
And gone away.
Suddenly the earth is dressed in green,
The trees and the vines in silver and green.

The swallows are back,
Building their nests beneath the eaves of the
      tower gates.

Farmers open the ground with their plows.
The little gray donkeys pull the harrow through it,
Drag the stone rollers over it.

The corn rains wake the earth;
The insects are stirred from their sleep;
The first faint thunder rouses the hibernating dragon.

The air is fragrant with spring.
It is the time for awakening.
The air is warm and full of drowsiness.
It is the time for not awakening,
It is the sleepy-moon.

—*Chinese*

The creeks and the streams and the Great River are full;
They flood beyond their banks.
The prairies are covered with water;
     the trees wade in it.
The mud robs a man of his moccasins
When he goes away from his wigwam.

The wolf and the fox and the buffalo are gone
     to dry land,
The turkey with them and the prairie chicken.

Man stays in the village,
Waits for the water to go back to the creeks
    and the streams and the Great River,
Waits for the earth to dry, for the air to warm
    in the sun.
He waits while the moon comes full and grows thin
    and comes full again.
This is the moon in which man has nothing to do.
This is the do-nothing-moon.

          —Illinois Indians (United States)

The season of planting is finished.
In the dry months the new land was cleared;
    the men did it.
They put in the plantains. The women set out
    the coco-yams,
Piled stones around to keep the porcupines from
    eating the tubers.

The melons are planted, and the maize.
The peppers are growing, the pineapples spread
    prickly leaves,
And the sugar cane sprouts.
The first weeds have been pulled.

The season of planting is finished.
This is the moon-in-which-men-throw-away-their-hoes.

                    —*Kpe (Central Africa)*

The Seven Stars are shining again.
Rejoice!
The high-born stars are in the eastern sky
Before the sunrise.

They announce the new year.
They begin the season of cool winds,
The first of the pleasant moons,
When man takes his ease.

The Seven Stars have been gone from the sky,
But they have returned.
This is the first moon,
The moon of Matariki,
The moon-of-the-Seven-Stars.

—*Pakapukan (Oceania)*

May

Night is almost gone,
Black night, and the gray half-light of day
Fade into pale yellow sunlight.

The ptarmigan that came in the last moon,
And perched near the houses, on the tree limbs,
Looking like great white fruits,
Have flown on north.

The willow saplings that hold up the turf roofs
Have sent out slender shoots,
And inside, the houses are thickets of green leaves.

The sled dogs sleep stretched full length in the
    warming air.
There is no ice on the cooking pots when the fires
    are out.

This is the end of winter.
This is the moon-when-the-ice-goes-out-of-the-rivers.

—Nunamiut (North Alaska Inland Eskimo)

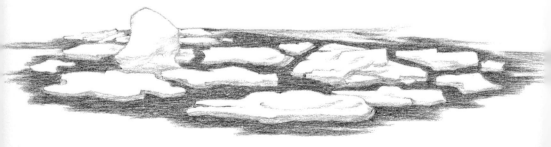

The food pits are empty.

The yams that were stored in them have been eaten.

There are only fern roots and wild cabbage for food.

The cuckoo has gone away and the winter star
    has risen.

The air is chill and the rain falls steadily.

There is nowhere to spin tops,
And the kites will not fly in the rain.
The houses are dark, for the doors and the windows
    stay shut against the rain.
They are filled with smoke from the charcoal fires
    that warm them.

Men grumble at the constant rain.

They grumble at the little food and the smoke
    in their eyes.

At night they grumble, forgetting the dance steps.

There is no one who does not grumble.

This is the grumbling-moon.

—*Maori (New Zealand)*

In the beginning man did not have cattle
Until God let down a strip of hide from heaven
And cattle came down to man.

God gave man grass for the cattle,
Put the Six Stars overhead to bring rain.
While they shine, there is much rain,
The grass is green, the cattle grow fat, man is rich.

When the Six Stars have set, it is the season of
      dryness, the time of little grass.
Yet, if it happens the black clouds stay in the sky
      and the heavy rains fall
Beyond the season of the shining of the Six Stars,
Man says, "We thought this was the first moon,
      the moon of the beginning of the year.
"It is not. We have forgotten."
"It is still the moon-in-which-the-Six-Stars-set."

                      —*Masai (Central Africa)*

The gentle winds blow,
The south winds, and the sea is untroubled.

The west winds are still;
The season of hurricanes is past.
The breadfruit trees that the winds laid down
Send their roots back into the earth.

It is the time for spinning coconut tops,
And flying candlenut leaves for kites.
The tame doves dart at the end of their tethers;
The fruit pigeons and parakeets nest in the
        coconut palms.

The air is still and dry.
It is filled with the chattering of birds.
They sing through the long day.
This is the moon-of-the-singing-birds.

—Samoan

There is no night.
The sun wanders in the sky,
Goes to the edge and feels the rim of it.

The clouds are rose flakes caught by the crags,
The plain of Thingvellir lies sleeping under
    flame-red mist.

The land rises, shadowy, green, out of the golden sea,
    Thor's land.

The summer flowers bloom on the stretching moorland;
The mountain torrents are foaming gold, the
      cataracts, and the geysers.

The dwarfs stay hid in the depths of the mountains,
And the giants keep away,
Lest the sun turn them to stone.

There is no night.
This is the nightless-moon.

—Icelandic

The giant cactus is ripe in the desert.
Its ancient arms, black against the crimson evening,
Are tipped with prickly fruit, like birds clustered.

With sharp blades on long poles the women
    harvest the fruit,
Gather the hard-shelled fruits, the fruits split in falling,
Cook them in clay pots, strain out the seeds
    with basket sieves,
Make rich red jam for eating,
Make thick red syrup for the Rain dance.

The whole village dances. In the Big House,
    around the ceremonial jars,
They dance and sing to give the cactus drink power,
So it will pull the rain from the clouds,
So the corn will grow and the squash and the beans.

They drink the bubbling juice when the Old Ones
    say it is ready,
Drink as the dry land drinks the rain that is coming;
Drink it for a sign, at the beginning of the new year,
In the moon of the Rain dance,
In the moon-of-the-giant-cactus.

             —*Pima (Southwestern United States)*

The grandfathers were instructed,
Taught how to use cedar bark,
How to make canoes of it, and build houses, and
    weave cloth of it.

The son of the town chief was taught,
But he carved whales from it,
Carved whales out of cedar bark, painted them
    black, threw them into the sea.

In the moon for gathering bark,
Men go to the island where the cedars stand,
And the whales come. They circle the island, fill
    the air with the noise of their blowing.

Men strip the bark from the trees, say of the sound,
"It is like the killer whale's blowing,"
Laugh, and say, *"This is the killer-whale-moon."*

—*Haida (Queen Charlotte's Island, B.C.)*

The hot sun has ripened the corn,
And the sweetness of the ears is in the air.
The messengers have been sent out to the fields.
They have brought back seven ripe ears.

The hunters have been in the woods,
And for six days they have hunted on the
     mountainside.

In the Principal Town a new fire has been lit
     on the altar,
Leaves of tobacco sprinkled on it,
Omens taken.

Now the feast begins, the summer feast.
This is the moon-of-the-new-ripe-corn.

       —*Cherokee (Southeastern United States)*

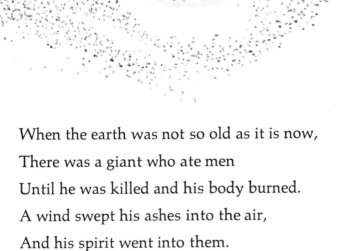

When the earth was not so old as it is now,
There was a giant who ate men
Until he was killed and his body burned.
A wind swept his ashes into the air,
And his spirit went into them.

Mosquitoes are the ashes of the cannibal monster,
The man-eating giant.
This is the moon the mosquitoes swarm,
This is the mosquito-moon.

—*Yukaghir (Northern Siberia)*

The dry fingers of the sun have wiped up the dampness
    around the grass roots,
And its hot fingers have seized coolness from under
    the trees.
The children go out from the village, down to the river,
    and come back.
They say to their parents, "The river is low enough.
We can wade in it."

Now the elders announce, "In four days we will go to gather gold."

On the fourth day, everyone goes out, and the
chief priest goes ahead

To the altar at the top of the sacred hill.
They pray to the spirits of the dead, and to the gods,
    for help.
They go back to their houses, each family to its own
    house, and pray to their ancestors for assistance.
They go down to the river, and wade in it, and dip pans
    into the water and pour it out.
Before the end of the day they have washed gold
    out of the river.
There is no one who has failed to find gold.
This is the moon-in-which-the-people-search-for-gold.

—*Melanesian (Timor)*

September

Beyond the Shining Mountains,
The wickiups stand on dry desert,
On barren ground where there is not enough
        rain for corn,
And melon vines shrivel without water.

Man gathers the seeds of wild grasses for food,
Digs their roots.
Hunts the hare and the gopher, the deer and antelope.
He digs trenches to trap crickets,
And broils them to eat.

He has no time to take from hunting and gathering
        and digging,
Little time for dancing,
Little food for feasting.

In the winter he names the moons,
Counts them to make them go quickly.

He does not name the summer moons
When there is more food to be found
And the bitter winds do not blow down the valley.

If he does not count the moons, or notice them,
It may be summer will not end.

This is a moon-without-a-name.

—*Northern Paiute Indians (Rocky Mountains)*

The villages stand on the lake-edge;
They are scattered in the river valleys,
On the morning side of the streams where
    the sun is pleasant,
On the summer slopes where the earth holds the rain
For redbud and digger pine and sumac,
For grasses and rushes
That man coils together, twines into baskets
    and sandals, makes into houses, canoes.

The villages stand in a kind and fruitful land.
Whatever man needs, already he has it.
So he thinks of the days coming,
Counts ahead, makes note of the next new moon,
Gives no name to this moon,
Says rather,
"The moon-after-this-moon-we-will-be-camping;
    we-will-be-gathering-acorns."

                —*Pomo Indians (California)*

The harvest is finished. Winter stays its coming.

It is the time the dead return from the world
    underground where they dwell.

It is time for food to be spread for them, and
    drink set out,

And their blessings sought on the barns and the
    stables, the fields and the forests.

It is the time for pranks and foolishness:

For masks cut out of birch bark

And curious costumes, and going about from house to

     house, calling out, "We are spirits," begging food.

It is the time for learning the future, overhearing
    the spirits talk,
Reckoning what will come from the fall of a
    slice of bread,
And a grain of salt melting,
And sticks burning in the oven.

It is the time when the dead walk the earth.
It is the moon-of-the-spirits.

—*Esthonian*

November

Cold flings itself out of the north,
Rushes on the wind across the bare earth,
Tears at the tent-skins with fingers of ice.

Day comes with the sun, but does not last long.
Night seizes the sky from it,
Piles blackness above the snow to the stars,
Peers through the smoke hole into the tent,
Steals under the reindeer skins and circles the fire.

The women sew while the daylight lasts.
They fashion skins into garments,

But now there is time only to make the thumb
    of a mitten,
So they say, "This is the season of the thumb,
"*This is the thumb-moon.*"

—*Ostiak Samoyed (Northern Siberia)*

The crops are in from the fields:
Rice and millet,
Beans and maize, pumpkins and gourds,
Chillies and onions, the leaves of herbs, drying . . .
Stored in the baskets and pots, on the shelves,
    hung above the hearth.

Now the women take clay and work it,

Roll it into balls, flatten it, pound it, add more clay to it,

Form wide-mouthed pots from it, with wide lips;

Make twin pots joined together, small pots
    with handles,
Ceremonial pots; fire them in the jungle in a wood fire.

When the harvest is in,
Before the cold begins,
Before the time of sowing comes,
The women make pots for storing, and cooking.
This is the earth-pot moon.

                    —Khasis (Northeastern India frontier)

The rice-cutting moons have gone,
And the moon when the animal tracks stay in the
     dust because there is no rain.
The cool winds are beginning to blow out of the north.

At night the thunderstorms come quickly,
And are gone, great drops of rain
Splashing in the dust,
Striking against the roof thatch,
Saying "Wa-la-wa-la-wa-la."
This is the wa-la-wa-la-moon.

—*Liberian (West Africa)*

Furry grandfather sleeps,
Bear, the winter sleeper is in his den.
The sun is gone, the long night has come.

The Yul people leave the hidden mountain, walk
   in the forests, sit in the tents.

Women make the Yul feast.
Men fashion ships of birch bark, with bark sails,
   and small oars.

They fill the ships with morsels of food: cheese,
　　and pieces of fowl from the feast.
They set the ships on the branches of tall trees,
And the Yul people eat.
They hang out containers of water,
　　and the Yul people drink.

The tents are still, without a sound in them.
Even the children are quiet.
Noise disturbs the Yul people, and they show
　　themselves to men.
Men fear the ghosts, fear the Yul people.

For twelve days the tents are silent,
　　while the Yul people feast.
This is the moon-of-Yul.

　　　　　　—Lapp (Northern Scandinavian peninsula)

NATALIA BELTING is an assistant professor of history at the University of Illinois, specializing in the French colonization of North America and the ethnohistory of the Illinois Indians.

The same interest in historical research which resulted in the distinguished *The Sun Is a Golden Earring,* has led Miss Belting to the folklore behind lunar calendars; legends which provide the background for her own interpretations of the moon-months. A poet as well as a researcher and teacher, Miss Belting has successfully combined these talents for her almanac of the CALENDAR MOON.

The author of several highly successful books for children, Miss Belting resides in Urbana, Illinois, where she enjoys gardening, cooking, and excavating ancient artifacts of the Illinois Indians from her own property. Miss Belting received a B.A. degree from Coe College, and an M.A. and Ph.D. from the University of Illinois.

BERNARDA BRYSON, whose illustrations for *The Sun Is a Golden Earring* were honored as runner-up to the 1963 Caldecott Award, is as well respected for her work in the field of art and illustration as is her husband, Ben Shahn.

Miss Bryson, whose drawings have appeared in *Fortune* and *Scientific American,* has illustrated several books for children, including one of her own.

Familiar with New Zealand, Southeast Asia, and Japan, and a frequent visitor to Europe, Miss Bryson is well qualified to interpret a collection of moon legends from all over the world.